Battling and Beating

THE DEMONS OF

DENTAL ASSISTING

How every dental assistant can have an amazing, fulfilling career

KEVIN HENRY, M.A.

INDIE BOOKS
INTERNATIONAL

No part of this publication may be reproduced or distributed in any form or by
any means without the prior permission of the publisher. Requests for permission
should be directed to permissions@indiebooksintl.com, or mailed to Permissions,
Indie Books International, 2424 Vista Way, Suite 316, Oceanside, CA 92054.

Neither the publisher nor the author is engaged in rendering legal or other
professional services through this book. If expert assistance is required, the services
of appropriate professionals should be sought. The publisher and the author shall
have neither liability nor responsibility to any person or entity with respect to any
loss or damage caused directly or indirectly by the information in this publication.

ISBN-10: 1-947480-05-7
ISBN-13: 978-1-947480-05-6
Library of Congress Control Number: 2017949766

Designed by Joni McPherson, mcphersongraphics.com

INDIE BOOKS INTERNATIONAL, LLC
2424 VISTA WAY, SUITE 316
OCEANSIDE, CA 92054
www.indiebooksintl.com

Contents

Preface

There's a saying: "If you love what you do, you'll never work a day in your life." I believe that to be true.

I love speaking to dental assistants and interacting with them. I've been lucky enough to do that for more than a decade, everywhere from Seattle to Boston and Phoenix to New Orleans. During my travels, however, I've seen dental assistants who are ready to give up and move on to another career. They're ready to quit because they have fallen out of love with their career. The light that burned so brightly when they first started as a dental assistant has been nearly snuffed out.

Those are the people who inspired me to write this book. Those are the people who were almost in tears after my courses because no one out there was speaking to them and listening to what they had to say. Those are the people, and they are *you*.

It's been my honor to meet so many of you over the years. It will be my honor to meet many more. But above all of that, it will be my greatest joy to hear your tales of success and overcoming the demons that I talk about in this book.

You inspired me to write this book. I hope I can inspire you to change the way you look at your career, starting today.

Let's slay these demons together, and then let's talk about it when you see me at the next trade show or online at IgniteDA.net. I'm happy to be your biggest cheerleader and fan.

I can't wait to hear your success stories.

> Kevin Henry
> May, 2017

Chapter 1

LAYING THE GROUNDWORK

If you're reading this book, I'm going to surmise one of two things. Either you're already a dental assistant, or you're thinking about becoming a dental assistant.

When I talk to dental assistants around the country, whether they've been an assistant for thirty years or thirty days, there is one constant. They love their patients. They may not love the paycheck. They may not love the drama that happens in their practices. They may not love a lot of things that are involved with their careers, but they love their patients.

Speaking as a dental patient, that is worth its weight in gold. You see, when we patients sit in your dental chair, we look to you as our confidant and the person we can trust. We see you as a person who will give us a straight answer to any question, including whether we really need a new crown (even though the dentist just told us we do).

That's a big responsibility. You have the attention of the patient, and he or she is looking to you to cement a big decision in his or her mind. Is that patient going to accept treatment or walk out the door and "think about it?"

A lot of that rests in your hands. If I'm the patient and I ask you, "What do you think?" when it comes to a new crown, or implant, or filling, or whatever the procedure might be, I'm not just asking you because I want your opinion. I'm asking you because I trust you.

This is a scenario that plays out in dental practices throughout the country every day of every week of every year. Patients look to you and want to trust what you say. They want to see confidence in your eyes. They want to see a reassuring smile on your face. They want to know their oral health is your priority.

That's no small task, and it's certainly not a task to be taken lightly. Are you up for the challenge?

The vast majority of you say "yes," and you show it every day in your work. You're not only there to be the advocate for your patient, but you're also there to be the glue that holds the entire practice together. Let's face it: if you call in sick, it's a bad day in the practice. No one else knows where any of the supplies are or when they need to be ordered. They also may have to actually remember how to take out the garbage and sterilize instruments. *Gasp*!

I remember one time when I was giving a lecture to dental assistants in Dallas. I actually had the entire team in my class: the dentist, hygienist, assistant, and office manager were all sitting there in the second row as I spoke for three hours about the importance of the dental assistant in the practice.

After the course was over, all four came up front to where I was standing and thanked me for the talk. One by one, starting with the dentist, then the hygienist, then the office manager, and finally the assistant, they each shook my hand and told me they had enjoyed my talk. It felt a bit like the receiving line at a wedding, but it was a nice moment.

As I shook the assistant's hand, she introduced herself, and these were her exact words: "Hi. Thanks for the talk. My name is Marcy, and I'm just the dental assistant."

She said this in a quiet tone and in an almost apologetic way; however, it was the "just" that stood out to me more than anything.

I politely pulled her aside from the rest of the team and told her that she should never say she was "just" the dental assistant again. She's *the* dental assistant. She's *the* backbone of the practice. She's *the* heartbeat of the practice. She's *the* person that many patients trust when they have a question or concern.

Dental assistants, I will tell you this: *You* have to have faith and confidence in yourself and in what you do. If you don't have confidence in yourself, who else is going to have confidence in you? It's a lesson that I've tried to teach to my daughter since the day she was born. It's a lesson I still try to instill in dental assistants in my talks throughout the nation.

If you do nothing else today, you must drop the word "just" from your vocabulary. A good friend of mine, Angela Severance, hosts a website for dental assistants called NINJAdentistry.com. Check it out. It's a great place where assistants are told how awesome they are (I love sites like that). But do you want to know what the best part about that whole site is? It's the name. You see, NINJA stands for, "No, I'm Not Just an Assistant." (OK, there's an extra A in there, but you get the point.) You're not just an assistant. You're a valuable piece of the puzzle, and one that the dental practice simply couldn't function without.

I always encourage dentists and dental team members

to view the practice as a small business. It's a small business just as much as a local restaurant or flower shop or veterinarian. Every member of the dental team (including the dentist) is an employee of that small business, known more affectionately as the dental practice. Every member of the dental team has a role to play in order for that business to do well.

Think about walking into your local coffee shop. There are usually two or three people who have a job to do to make sure you walk out with the right cup of coffee. At the very least, there's a person who takes the order and a person who fulfills the order. If they don't do their jobs right, it's likely you're going to find somewhere else to get that cup of coffee in the morning.

The same is true for the dental practice. You have customers (patients) who come into your small business every day. How they are treated and their level of satisfaction will determine whether they come back for that root canal or six-month checkup. If they don't come back, your business suffers. If the business suffers, you as a worker suffer. It's not a pretty picture or cycle.

You see, the business of the practice doesn't just affect the doctor and whether he or she can make his next car payment (which is what the patient always thinks, right?). It's also about whether you can make your next car payment as well. It's about your family having the things you want them to have. It's about knowing that, at the end of the day, you're playing a key role in a business that is not only doing well financially but also changing lives.

And changing lives is why so many of you became assistants, right? You wanted to help Mrs. Jones smile again. You wanted to make sure that oral cancer is caught as early as possible. You want to watch when that teenager has his braces taken off and a big smile spreads across his face.

Those are just some of the moments that make you glad you're an assistant. I've seen the looks in your eyes when you've told me those stories. I know how much your patients mean to you. Those are the moments that make you smile, and we're going to talk a lot about those. There are also moments that make you cringe and grit your teeth and wonder why you ever became a dental assistant. We're going to talk about those as well.

I believe strongly that dental assisting can be an amazing career for anyone who chooses it as their vocation. It's not just a stepping stone to hygiene. It's not just a job. It's a career where you can find joy and fulfillment.

So, why should you enjoy your career as an assistant? There are plenty of reasons for that, some of which we've already highlighted. But to enjoy your career, you have to know how to navigate through some of the minefields and pitfalls that have already claimed so many of your colleagues. That's where we're heading in the following chapters.

You are a rock-star dental assistant. You are an amazing asset to your business. Believe in yourself and believe in the power you have.

Remember the scene near the end of *The Wizard of Oz*, in which Glinda tells Dorothy she doesn't need to help her any longer?

Glinda: You don't need to be helped any longer.

You've always had the power to go back to Kansas.

Dorothy: I have?

Scarecrow: Then why didn't you tell her before?

Glinda: She wouldn't have believed me. She had to learn it for herself.[1]

I believe the same thing about assistants. You've always had the power to change lives inside of you. Sometimes, however, you need to go on a journey to discover that.

I hope this book will be your journey and you'll discover the power that's always been inside you. When you do, you will love your dental assisting career more than you ever thought possible.

---

[1] "Movie Quote DB." Movie Quotes Database. Accessed May 10, 2017. http://www.moviequotedb.com/movies/wizard-of-oz-the/quote_26339.html.

Chapter 2

FINDING THE EASTER EGGS

THE OPPOSITE OF WISDOM TEETH . . .

CURLY   LARRY   MOLA

So, how do you succeed in your career as a dental assistant? How do you truly enjoy every day? How do you overcome some of the stuff you deal with on a daily basis in your business? You have to look for the Easter eggs.

What do I mean by that?

I know not all of you will celebrate the holiday, but Easter was a big day in our house when my daughter was growing up.

Sure, Christmas was great and her birthday was fun, but my daughter loved nothing more than hunting Easter eggs when she was little. To her, the joy of discovering a hidden treasure of coins or chocolate in the grass or behind a plant was one of the greatest things ever. The look on her face when she found an egg and opened it was priceless.

For me, as a dad, I loved hiding the eggs. Of course, as she got older, trying to outsmart her and hide eggs where she couldn't so easily find them became more and more difficult. It also became increasingly difficult for me to remember where I had hidden them all. Sometimes, yes, I outsmarted myself.

As Easter recently approached this year, I thought back to those days with fond memories. My daughter is nineteen now, and the days of hiding eggs seem like a lifetime ago.

But I started thinking about all of the hidden joys that we discover from time to time in our lives that can make us as giddy as my daughter was when she found an Easter egg.

Often, in our day-to-day activities, we get caught in a rut. Yesterday seems like the day before, which seemed like the day before. We don't take the time to try to find the little things that can change up our routines. We don't see the value in digging a little deeper to find that reward. If it's not right in front of us, sometimes we miss the greatest rewards.

You may not hunt for eggs on Easter weekend (or any weekend, for that matter), but how would it change your day or career if you started looking for little moments of joy every day in your practice? Maybe it's a patient you love to see, or a patient who is getting ready to have his or her smile changed forever. Maybe it's an opportunity to pitch an idea on how your business can do things better. Maybe it's actually implementing the idea and seeing it become a reality.

Whatever it is, you simply have to look around to find

hidden joys in your career. They may not always be easy to find, but that makes the discovery even sweeter.

People often ask me why I became so passionate about dental assistants and the role they play in the practice. It's simple, really. When I first came into the dental industry in 1999, I started in a role as managing editor for *Dental Economics* magazine right after leaving the world of sports public relations. Now *that's* a switch in careers.

I knew nothing about dentistry outside of the procedures I had experienced as a patient through the years. I knew if I was going to really know my new audience, I had to go inside the dental practice and learned how it really worked.

I went into numerous practices and talked to people about what happened behind the scenes on a normal day. I watched. I listened. I observed. I took tons of notes. What I quickly found was that the dental assistant played a pivotal role, not only helping the team get through the day, but actually helping them do it with less stress. The dental assistant held a key role in the practice, yet when I looked at publications and resources out there, very few were for the dental assistant. Everyone wanted to talk to the dentist or hygienist; what about the assistant?

That's why I pushed to start *Dental Assisting Digest*, a monthly newsletter for assistants. I worked on several publications when I was with PennWell (the parent company for *Dental Economics*), but nothing gave me more joy than putting together this monthly newsletter and helping dental assistants see how powerful they truly were.

Since then, I have spoken to assistants everywhere, from Seattle to Boston and all points in between. When I step in front of assistants, I do so with a simple message: "You matter, and here's how and why." The way their faces light up and smiles break out gives me goose bumps.

Boiled down to its very essence, it's all about belief and taking steps to show people you truly believe you're a rock-star assistant and the backbone of the practice. Yes, it's going to take some courage on your part to make that happen. Yes, it's going to take some hard work and dedication to your career. Yes, it's going to take some education. In the end, however, the emotional rewards will be far worth the work you've put in.

I wish that every assistant could meet my friend Tija Hunter, who works in the St. Louis area. She is an assistant who understands the importance of taking that extra step when it comes to her career. If you Google her name, you will see more credentials after her name than you will care to count. She calls herself an "education geek." I call her a great example of how to pursue your career more deeply and always stay ahead of the curve.

Here's what Tija told me as her advice on education for assistants:

> "To me, it's about not just staying current. It's about staying at the forefront of what I do. I could sit back every day and do fine with what I already know. But what happens when a patient asks me a question and I might not know the answer? I don't want that. I want to know the answers because I learned the question before the patient even asked me."

That's finding the Easter egg.

I've seen assistants like Tija, and I've seen assistants who are the complete opposite. I've seen assistants who are passionate about what they do, and I've seen plenty who just punch the clock and get the paycheck and go home. Obviously, I want to see you be the former, and not the latter.

I remember when my daughter was little she and I were heading from Tulsa to Dallas to spend New Year's Eve with some friends of ours. We stopped at Turner Falls Park, not far from the Oklahoma-Texas state line. (Yes, if you're wondering, there actually is a waterfall in Oklahoma. It's a place that she always loved to visit, and she still loves to go there now that she is attending college at the University of Oklahoma.)

On this crisp, sun-drenched day, my daughter and I were almost the only two people at the park. We walked to the waterfall and back and then just hung out and threw some rocks in the stream coming off the waterfall. It was a great day, not only weather-wise, but also in terms of making memories.

I vividly remember looking at the stream and observing

how clear it was. Then, just past the stream, I noticed a pool of water that had been cut off from the ever-flowing water from the waterfall. This pool of water was, for lack of a better word, nasty. Scum was growing on the top, and you could almost hear the flies buzzing around it. It was not the place you wanted to be and especially not that close to the nearby nice stream.

That view got me thinking about the two types of dental assistants in the world. There are those who are ever-changing, evolving, and eager to learn new things. They're moving ahead, and they're the type of people who you want to be around and have as a part of your business. Then there are the assistants who are stagnant. They've done the same thing the same way for countless months or years, and they're not going to change any time soon. New technology? *Bah; it's just a fad*, they may grumble. These assistants aren't the kind of employees who are going to move your business forward.

Which kind of assistant do you want to be? It seems like a question with an obvious answer. But that's where the rut of doing things the same way every day can pull you in, and sometimes without your even knowing it. That's where you have to look and find your Easter eggs. Find what gives you joy during the day. Find what you can learn to expand your career. Ask questions of your sales rep, dentist, or fellow assistants. One of the best ways to move forward is to sometimes take a step into the great unknown.

The inspirational author Shannon Alder once said, "Sometimes taking a leap of faith requires an imaginative mind that can create the ending you are unable to see." What ending do you want to see every day at your business? You can make it happen. You just have to be willing to put forth the effort to make it a reality.

Now, let's start slaying some of the demons that keep you from those possibilities.

Chapter 3

THE DEMON OF MONEY

I CAN'T READ YOUR HANDWRITING, DOCTOR. DOES OUR PATIENT HAVE PLAQUE OR THE PLAGUE?

GLASBERGEN
©Glasbergen

When I am lecturing to dental assistants, I often give advice on "battling and beating the demons of dental assisting." That has been and continues to be my course title for many years now. It rang true with many assistants, because every day can be a struggle against things that, if you don't figure out a way to move past them or improve them, will haunt you.

We're going to talk about those demons and how you can beat them in the next five chapters. The very first demon we're going to tackle is the one that is a pain point for many dental assistants: money.

As I said in Chapter 1, you didn't get into the dental assisting field to get rich. You did it because you wanted to help people. That's a noble cause, but it doesn't fill up your bank account. I often say that dental assistants make a choice to pursue a passion over their pocketbook.

Have you ever wondered how your salary stacks up against other assistants in your state or around the country? There's an easy way to find out. The Bureau of Labor Statistics tracks salaries for every profession you can think of on their site at www.bls.gov. With just a few clicks, you can see how much dental assistants make in your state. You can also compare those numbers to what hygienists and dentists make in your state, as well. All of the numbers are tabulated by tax returns, and I haven't found a more reliable source for salary information than this site.

According to 2016 statistics (the latest published as of the writing of this book), Minnesota is the state that pays assistants the most in the country ($22.70 per hour), while West Virginia has the dubious honor of being the state with the lowest average hourly rate for assistants ($13.42, which is actually down from the $14.08 published in 2014).

Yes, a few hundred miles within our great nation can make a huge difference.

One of the most common questions I am asked during my lectures is how dental assistants can make more money. Hey, who among us wouldn't like to increase our salary, right? I'll give you some thoughts on that in just a moment. But first, humor me by reading two of my favorite quotes of all time.

John Ruskin, one of the great visionaries of the 19th century, once wrote, "In order that people may be happy in their work, these three things are needed: they must be fit for it; they must not do too much of it; and they must have a sense of success in it."[2]

---

[2]   Ruskin, John, and J. M. W. Turner. *Pre-Raphaelitism*. New York: Alden, 1885.

Then there's this great quote, widely attributed to the late TV host Johnny Carson: "Never continue in a job you don't enjoy. If you're happy in what you're doing, you'll like yourself; you'll have inner peace. And if you have that, along with physical health, you will have had more success than you could possibly have imagined."

One thing to note in both of those quotes is this: both talk about happiness, but never mention money once. Both, however, mention success, and I think that's where dental assistants must focus.

What is it that drives you? If it's money, I'll give you some tips in a moment, but let me also warn you that, ultimately, this isn't the field for you. If it's a sense of success, I'll give you some tips on that as well.

Don't get me wrong. I absolutely believe you should be paid well for what you do; however, I don't believe any of us (myself included) are ever going to be paid what we're truly worth. That's just not how business works, and you do work for a business. Never forget that.

So, what's the key equation to making more money,

you ask? My friend (and a huge champion for dental assistants), Linda Miles, once told me in order for assistants to make more money, the equation needs to be broken down into four parts.

- Twenty-five percent of one's merit increase is based on *attitude.*

- Twenty-five percent of a merit increase is based on the employee's scope of responsibility.

- Twenty-five percent of the merit increase is based on the employee's performance evaluation, which is completed in three ways: doctor's evaluation, self-evaluation, and peer review.

- The most important 25 percent, which impacts the other three, is the health of the practice in the past twelve months.

Let's look at each of those points, starting first with attitude.

I spoke once to a group of dental assistants in upstate New York, and one of the assistants started telling me about a hygienist in her practice named Patti. Now, the way this assistant talked about Patti, you would think she had horns growing out of the top of her head. Everything Patti did, everything Patti said, and every breath that Patti had ever breathed was pure evil—at least according to this assistant.

It became clear to me that this woman was letting Patti ruin her life. I have some advice for that in the next chapter. Since that day, however, I've always asked assistants one simple question: "Are you the Patti of your business?"

Are you the person about whom people talk behind the scenes sarcastically as "Little Miss Sunshine?" Do your coworkers dread hearing your latest angst-filled tale? That's where your attitude comes into play.

Your attitude can translate to your patients as well. No one wants to be around someone who is always complaining or griping, especially someone who is walking into your business (where he or she may not exactly be comfortable anyway).

Think honestly about the attitude you bring to the practice every day. If there's room for improvement, make that improvement immediately.

The next 25 percent is based on your scope of responsibility. What do you do in the business to help the business succeed? Have you ever thought about that question? I encourage you to make a list of everything you do in the practice on a daily basis. Even if you think it's a menial task, write it down.

Also, do you know everything you legally can or can't do in the practice? There's an easy way to find out. Every state has different rules for assistants, and you have to know that you are doing what you're supposed to do. The Dental Assisting National Board (DANB) has put together an easy way for you to know what you legally can and can't do in the practice. Visit www.DANB.org and look under the *Meet State Requirements* tab.

This brings up two interesting points. First, if you see something on the list you can legally do in your state, but you're not currently doing it, that is a great opportunity to have a talk with your dentist. Ask him or her why you're not doing it in your practice. It's a question that's not meant to be an interrogation, but rather a business-related inquiry. If you're thinking about your practice as a business, why shouldn't you, as an employee, be doing everything you can to help the bottom line of the business? Maybe you need additional training. Maybe the practice manager never knew you could assume responsibility for a certain procedure (trust me, not all dentists know what their assistants are capable of doing). By asking this question, you're not only starting the wheels turning on improving the bottom line, but also showing you're invested emotionally in the success of the business.

OK, so, what if you look on the DANB list and see that you're doing something in the practice that you're legally not allowed to do in your state? Then it's time to have an honest, open talk with your dentist. This is for your protection. If an audit was ever done in your practice, or something ever went wrong with one of your patients, guess who would share some of the blame in court? Yes, you. And ignorance is not a valid excuse.

If the dentist didn't know you were doing something illegally, great. Things can be changed. However, if the dentist did knowingly have you doing something illegal, it's probably time for you to ask if that's the type of business with which you want to be involved. You have to protect yourself and your family. Knowledge is the best way to make that happen.

The next 25 percent involves the performance evaluation. I believe you need to have an evaluation by your dentist at least annually. I think it's vital for you to talk about your strengths and what you can improve upon. This is a business discussion, not an emotional discussion. This is a discussion that should happen in order for the business to run at an optimal level. It's also a chance to open the lines of communication between you and your dentist even further.

I know not every dentist is going to want to have this conversation. Dentists often think performance evaluations revolve exclusively around money, and that makes them uncomfortable. I get that. However, this isn't just a conversation about how you can be paid more. It's also a conversation about how the business can run more smoothly.

Here are the three things you need to bring to your evaluation.

1. **The list of everything you do in the practice on a daily basis, which I told you to draw up earlier.** If the length of that list surprised you, it will also surprise the dentist, who may not have any idea how much you do to help the business on a daily or weekly basis.

2. **A sharp ear and a sharp pencil.** Listen and take notes. Refer back to these notes as your action plan for helping to move your career forward and become better at what you do. They are also valuable for the next time you have an evaluation, so you can show how you've stepped up for the business and your career.

3. **A plan for the finale.** Look, let's be honest.

This conversation is either going to go better than you think or worse than you think. You have to be emotionally prepared for either scenario. If you're not, emotions can override the business purpose for the review. If the conversation turns emotional, everyone loses. Keep your emotions in check and remember, "It's all about business."

The last 25 percent revolves around the business numbers of the practice. As my friend Linda Miles says, "It's hard to play a game if you don't know the score." It's also hard for an assistant to think about a raise if the business isn't doing well. More than likely, it's not going to happen under those circumstances.

If you don't know how your practice is doing on a monthly basis, ask. It's important for you, as an employee of the business and a key part of the business's success, to know the score. If the practice is doing great that month, awesome. Keep doing what you're doing. If it's struggling, show your leadership skills by coming up with some ideas about how it can be improved. Maybe it's a new procedure that could be incorporated, or a new skill you could learn. Show your investment in the business's success by suggesting ideas and coming up with a plan.

What if your doctor won't share the numbers with you? Perhaps that's a sign that he or she doesn't understand the concept of the entire team having a significant role to play in the success of the business. It's worth a conversation (show your initiative here) and if he or she still isn't willing to part with the numbers, decide whether that is a dealbreaker for you at this stage of your career.

I want to make one thing very clear. I never tell assistants they should quit their jobs. Ever. However, if there are enough red flags that you don't enjoy what you do, or you dread waking up every day to go to work, life is too short to live like that. Some kind of change must be made.

If you've looked at all four portions of the equation and all systems seem green, then it's an appropriate time to have the money conversation with your dentist. Be armed with information rather than emotion. Form the conversation around the business, not your needs. If you're going to be viewed as a respected team member and leader in your business, this is the perfect time to show those traits.

Does it always work? Do assistants always get a raise? Absolutely not. But this plan gives you the best base for potential success.

If you don't get the raise, ask yourself if money is the main motivator for what you do every day. Are you happy where you are? Do you like the people with whom you work? Do you feel valued and important? Do you feel like you're making a difference where you are? These are key questions to ask.

If you had to choose, would you pick a big paycheck with a lot of stress over a smaller paycheck with low levels of stress? Most of the people I know would choose the latter over the former. Which would you pick?

Your paycheck can be a demon that gnaws at you, day after day after day. If it is, slay that demon by following a systematic plan and having business conversations as soon as possible. You may find it tough to get the ball rolling, but it's better than letting your salary control your happiness.

Chapter 4

THE DEMON OF RESPECT

W hat's the most important seven-letter word to a dental assistant, but is one of the hardest to acquire at times? Respect. It's absolutely one of the biggest demons that assistants battle on a daily basis. Assistants often believe they are on the lowest rung on the ladder or the lowest position on the totem pole of the business. As you already know from reading the first three chapters of this book, however, I think nothing is further from the truth.

Jackie Robinson, the baseball player who broke the color barrier in 1947, once said, "I'm not concerned with your liking or disliking me. All I ask is that you respect me as a human being."[3] Really, that's what any of us want on a daily basis. Respect my opinions. Respect who I am. Respect what I believe. Respect that I am a valuable employee of this business.

It sounds simple, right? Yet we all know that it's anything but simple. There are actually some very important things to remember about gaining respect from other people.

You Don't Deserve It Until You Earn It

You know the people who walk into the room and seem to think they immediately own the place, or that they've immediately become the most important person in that room just by their presence? Don't be that person. No one respects that person, no matter what he or she thinks.

---

[3]   Pulis, Fred. *The Impact and Legacy Years*, 1941, 1947, 1968. Victoria, B.C.: Trafford, 2000, p. 20.

You earn respect every day by your actions and living up to what you say. You earn respect every day by doing your job and not complaining about what you do or how you do it. You earn respect by what you bring to the bottom line of the business.

If you're doing your job every day and then making sure to let everybody know you're doing your job, that's not earning their respect.

> "Yep, I just took out the garbage . . . *again*."

> "Guess who just talked Mrs. James down off the ledge when she was scared about her root canal?"

> "Who has two thumbs and just recorded the fastest intraoral scan of her career? That's right; it's me."

No. Don't do any of those. Learn your craft and be the best you can be, but don't tell everyone about it.

Take Care of Your Own Business

It's easy to get caught up in office drama, isn't it? It's so easy to listen to Betty talk about Cindy and all of her problems. But when you're doing that, you're taking away time and energy from what you should be doing in the business.

Gossip and cliques in the practice benefit no one. They are huge wastes of time and can cause distractions and hurt feelings that your patients will notice.

This may already be happening in your practice. At a recent American Association of Dental Office Management (AADOM) meeting I attended, one of the most popular courses was about deflating gossip in the practice. Every practice deals with this problem.

It takes a big person to walk away from a gossip session. It takes a bigger person to put a stop to it and try to bring coworkers back to the important tasks at hand. Are you that person?

Remember, you're an employee of the business with a list of tasks to perform every day. So is everyone else, from the dentist to the person handling the front desk. If you can keep your business front and center, you'll help diffuse any rifts that might be forming. The quicker they stop, the quicker everyone can finish their tasks and be done for the day.

Always Go One Step Further

For a dental assistant, this may seem like common sense. After all, the assistant is often the first to come into the practice in the morning and the last to leave; however, I'm talking about going one step further in your career as well.

What's the next class you can take? What's the next designation you can earn? What's the next technique you can learn? There's an entire world of possibilities out there. What will you tackle next?

Be Good at What You Do

You can probably think of people who just skate by and do as little as they can during the day. They're just coming to work to earn some money, and they couldn't care less about any enjoyment or pleasure they could derive from their craft.

Those who take the extra step to further their career are not only the ones who enjoy what they do more. They're also the people who are respected for their work ethic and dedication.

What can you do today to become the best dental assistant you can be?

Conduct Yourself Professionally

Have a good attitude. Don't be a gossip. Don't huff and puff every time you're asked to do something. Don't be someone who slides into the business at the last minute.

During my early days in the industry, we had a meeting dedicated to dental assistants called "Professional Dental Assisting." We thought it was important to set the tone for the meeting from the moment it was designed by putting the word "Professional" in the title. We wanted to focus on what it took for assistants to take their careers to the proverbial "next level." Being a professional is a big step toward that.

As I always tell assistants, you're not *just* an assistant. One of the many things you are is a health care professional. If you want respect, you have to believe you're a professional and act the part before anyone else will start to view you in that manner.

Be Yourself

If there's one pet peeve I have above all others, it's people who are two-faced. They act like they love you when they're talking to you but will stab you in the back the second they walk away. When someone is like this, you simply can't trust him or her, because you never know whether he or she is going to be your friend or your enemy that day.

When I say, "Be yourself," I'm imploring you to be the person you are deep down. Don't act like someone else, and don't act fake. We all can spot a fake person a mile away, right?

Sure, there are days when we all have to slap a smile on our face to get through, but that shouldn't be *every* day. You should be the same person in the business that you are when you're at the grocery store or football game. If you're not, what's keeping you from being consistent with your attitude throughout the day?

Let Your Actions Be a Role Model for Others

I believe wholeheartedly that dental assistants can be leaders in the dental practice. I don't care about your pay grade or the formal organizational setup in your business. I believe your actions can set the tone for the day with your coworkers.

If you refuse to give into gossip, you're setting an example. If you do things without complaining or announcing how great you are, you're setting an example. If you're coming up with ideas that can improve the business, you're setting an example.

In addition to setting an example, when you do these things, you're also growing your confidence to handle any situation. The importance of that can't be underestimated.

Have you seen the picture of a kitten sitting in front of the mirror, and the reflection in the mirror is a lion? Confidence is about how you perceive yourself every day. If you think you're a leader, you'll be just that.

I have had many assistants tell me that it's hard for them to get any kind of respect in the practice because of the way they are treated by the dentist. If you're in this situation, here's my advice.

My grandpa never went to school past elementary school, yet he was one of the smartest men I ever met. I think about him every day and still miss him, though he's been gone twenty-five years now. One day when I was in high school, I was griping to him about my football coaches, who kept harping on me that I wasn't blocking properly on a certain play. All I could think about was how wrong these coaches were. After all, I was seventeen. I had to be doing everything perfectly, right?

I'll never forget what he told me that day. With a big wad of tobacco in his mouth and his baseball cap pulled down, he looked at me and said, "You know, criticism is a path to opportunity."

I shook my head at his attempt at logic. It wasn't until years later that I finally figured it out and understood what he had been trying to tell me.

If I had taken my own emotions out of the equation and actually listened to what the coaches were saying, I might have understood the issue a lot more, and might have actually been able to concentrate on getting better at what I did (blocking was a pretty key thing for an offensive lineman to be able to do, even in high school).

The same could be said for you. If you listen to what is really being said, will you find an opportunity to improve in your career? If you strip the emotion out of the conversation, is there some truth to what is being said to you?

You may think you're the best in the world at taking impressions. However, your dentist is asking you to take a class on it at the next convention. *What?* That's crazy. You're the best at this. What could you possibly learn?

Well, do you know how many remakes are coming back from the lab? Do you know how many times one of your impressions has had a flaw that caused extra work on someone else's part? Do you know the real facts behind what is being said?

Criticism is indeed a path to opportunity. Listen. Learn. Think. Grow your career. Earn respect. It's not always the easiest road, but for a health care professional like yourself, it's the only road to travel.

Chapter 5

THE DEMON OF COMPLACENCY

GOOD DENTAL HYGIENE IS IMPORTANT FOR THE WHOLE FAMILY . . . BUT FLOSSING YOUR CAT WAS PROBABLY A BAD IDEA.

GLASBERGEN

©Glasbergen / glasbergen.com

My friend Cathy Jameson is a well-known dental consultant and one of the most amazing women you'll ever meet. She's also a fellow Oklahoman, so we share that bond as well.

Cathy has a great quote on putting your action plan together that I wanted to share with you.

"Feedback is vital to the growth of an employee," Jameson said. "People want feedback. They want to know when things are going well and when they need to improve. No one wants to be doing a job poorly. Give people the respect they deserve by speaking to them in a proactive, constructive manner."

One of the best ways that you can put together an action plan to push your career forward is to listen to the feedback you've received on your job. Again, boil the emotions out of it and think about this in a business setting. What are you doing well? What can you improve upon? What skills do you need to improve upon what you're already doing?

Knowing the answers to these questions can help you formulate a plan for your career. If you don't have a plan for where you want to go, you're never going to get there. Complacency is a demon that I often see short-circuiting the careers of dental assistants. They know they want to go somewhere and do something. They just can't tell you where or what.

When my daughter was little, one of her favorite movies

was *Alice in Wonderland*. There's a great scene in there where the Cheshire Cat is trying to learn more about Alice and her goals.

Here is their exchange.

> Alice: "Which road do I take?"
>
> Cheshire Cat: "Where do you want to go?"
>
> Alice: "I don't know."
>
> Cheshire Cat: "Then it doesn't matter. If you don't know where you are going, any road will get you there."[4]

That's what I see frequently with dental assistants. They head down a road without really knowing what the destination is supposed to be and end up frustrated in their career because it seems the road they have chosen is just a big circle; they keep going back to their starting point or never progressing very far.

To get past the demon of career roadblocks, you have to have a plan in place. Think about where you want to

---

[4] *Alice in Wonderland*. Produced by Walt Disney. 1951. DVD.

be in three months, six months, one year, and five years. Be realistic, but also stretch your boundaries a little bit. To say, "I want to be working for Dr. Smith" isn't much of a stretch if you're already working for Dr. Smith. He may be the best dentist in the world, but you're already working there. It's a pretty easy box to check.

Think about your career and what you want to learn. Certainly, you may still want to be working for Dr. Smith, but in what way? What if you still want to be working in that practice, but have your expanded functions designation? What if you still want to be beside Dr. Smith, but you want to be completely updated on the latest technology available to your business? Maybe you're fascinated by intraoral scanning. What do you need to do to become proficient in this up-and-coming technology?

Perhaps your goal is not to be working with Dr. Smith, but to land at another business where your skills are valued even more than they already are. Perhaps Dr. Smith is never going to get the technology you think the business should acquire. That could be a dealbreaker for you, and you believe you need to find another practice where technology is the focal point of patient care. Perhaps this is where you want your career to go. How are you going to get there? What steps do you need to take to make that transition?

Obviously, that's a bigger to-do on the list; it's going to take some planning and courage. Don't let the fact that something that seems hard keep you from doing it. Often, we as human beings go into the fetal position if we think something is going to take a lot of work or be difficult to do.

Civil rights leader Dr. Martin Luther King once said, "Faith is taking the first step even when you don't see the whole staircase."[5] Whatever you want to have on your list, it's going to take some work and effort. Taking the first step on that journey is all you need to do to get started. Then take the next step, and the one after that. Have a plan in place and methodically map it out and follow it. When you do that, you'll be amazed how far

---

[5] "MLK Quote of the Week: Faith Is Taking the First Step..." Home | The Martin Luther King Jr. Center for Nonviolent Social Change. February 21, 2013. http://www.thekingcenter.org/blog/mlk-quote-week-faith-taking-first-step.

you can advance your career with a plan in place.

We've talked in the previous chapter about earning respect in the practice. Having respect from your teammates and having a sense of confidence in yourself is key to moving your career forward.

Let's say becoming one of the leaders of your practice is on your list. Let me share with you an example of what an assistant did to demonstrate the power she wielded in her practice to make the business better.

You know as well as I do that patients can ask the same question to multiple people in the practice just to see if there's an answer that they might like better or could fit into their lifestyle a little more. If you've ever had a patient who just had a new filling placed ask you how long until he or she can chew on that side, you know what I'm talking about. Maybe your patients have a lunch coming up shortly, and to hear they can't chew before noon just doesn't work for them, so they may not only ask *you* how soon they can eat, but also the front desk person and/or even the dentist, as well.

Yes, patients expect you to have immediate answers to their basic questions. Yes, they may not like the answer to those questions, so they may ask around until they hear the answer they like. Here's what a practice in upstate New York did.

The assistant in that business suggested to her entire team that the team track the common questions that patients asked on a daily basis. (You know that you get asked the same question multiple times during the day, so take a note of those mentally.)

At this practice's morning huddle, the assistant started the discussion about these common questions and suggested that, as a group, they come up with some scripting that everyone on the team, from the front office to the back, would know when they were asked a question. They came up with ten questions and, as a team, developed the practice's standard answers to those questions.

This not only helped to solve a problem in their business, but also reinforced the important role that assistant played in the practice. It also reinforced to her that she could not only come up with brilliant ideas, but also that those ideas would be embraced by the rest of her team.

As I've noted before, slaying demons is all about having a business discussion in your practice. Think about the ways that you can impact the bottom line of the business and let those be your guideposts along your career path.

Of course, not every idea you throw out is going to be accepted. They may be rejected. You may even get some of *those* looks from other team members. That's fine. Don't let one rejection keep you from rising to the role of leader or keep you from continuing down the career path you've established in your mind.

I am a list person. I like to write things down and cross them off the list as they're completed. I not only have a daily list, but also a monthly list and goals for myself to complete by the end of the year. I find that lists like these not only keep me on track, but also serve as a gratifying reward when I accomplish one of the tasks I've written down. There's something about crossing a to-do off the list that is very fulfilling to me.

Lists can be a great way for you to visualize where you want to go in your career, give you a method to ensure you're staying on track, and get the important things done to push you down that road.

You've invested time, energy and money to get to where you currently are in your career. Don't let the demon of complacency keep you from realizing your full potential as an assistant. Think about your goals. Write them down. Make a plan to become the best dental assistant that you can possibly be. Don't be afraid to offer ideas and rise to the role of leader in your business. You can do it. You just have to know which road you're going down.

Chapter 6

THE DEMON OF GETTING ALONG

GLASBERGEN

"No, the Tooth Fairy is not running a ponzi scheme."

We recently marked the twenty-fifth anniversary of the 1992 Los Angeles riots, which erupted after four white police officers were acquitted of using excessive force after they were videotaped beating African-American motorist, Rodney King. I don't know about you, but watching the city of Los Angeles explode in racial hatred and anger in 1992 was something that seemed surreal to this young adult who was living miles away in Oklahoma. Images on the television showing all of the fires and destruction during that time were something that I couldn't stop watching, and couldn't believe was actually happening.

I recently talked about the L.A. riots to my daughter, who is currently nineteen. She looked at me as if that was ancient history. Of course, it happened before she was born; the thought of that immediately made me feel very, very old.

The same may be true for many of you. The events of 1992 may seem as distant as the events of 1492, when Christopher Columbus landed in America. If that's you, I encourage you to go back and look at not only the days that unfolded before my eyes over 2,000 miles away, but also at the events that led up to the riots, looting, and fires.

For many of us, when we think about the L.A. riots of 1992, we think about Rodney King. His famous line, "Can't we all just get along?" became a symbol of that horrific time.

Today, we are still asking ourselves that question. *Can't we all just get along?* It often seems that race relations haven't improved much in our country since 1992. That, however, is a discussion for a whole other book at a whole other time.

Can't we all just get along?

That may be a question that you ask yourself every day when you walk into the dental practice. If you're working in a single-doctor facility, just five or six of you may comprise the team. For some of you, that's your reality. Others may have ten coworkers, or twenty, or more. But it doesn't matter how many coworkers you have; sometimes it's simply impossible to get along.

So, can't we all just get along? The simple answer is no; we can't. We're human beings, and each of us has different things that we like or don't like, different teams that we root for or hate, and different things that we enjoy or drive us absolutely up the wall.

My dad has rarely used a toothpick. I'm convinced of that fact. How do I know? For as long as I can remember, he's made this sucking sound through his teeth trying to dislodge food after a meal. You know the sound. You've heard it before, I'm sure. It's a sound that bothers me, but absolutely drives my daughter up the wall.

When my mom, my dad, my daughter, and I used to go to lunch after church on Sunday, I knew what was coming in the car on the ride home. From the backseat, I would start hearing sucking sounds as my dad finished off the last bits of his meal. I was driving, but could peek at my daughter in the passenger seat and almost literally watch her skin crawl.

There are things that all of us do that annoy someone else. Sometimes, these are things we can move past and let roll off our backs. But there are plenty of times that a certain sound, saying, or action make our skin crawl as well.

Are you facing that in your practice today? Is there something happening that is bothering you and keeping you from enjoying your day? Then it has to stop today. Not tomorrow, but today.

Maybe it's not a sound or a saying. Maybe people keep

leaving dirty dishes in the sink or not cleaning up after themselves in the break room. Maybe people don't think it's their job to put away supplies or clean instruments. Maybe they don't think they should ever have to seat a patient. Whatever it is, it bugs you, and it sometimes eats you alive. What is it that bothers you every day in your business?

Here's my simple take on what you should do: talk to the person about it. I know, you think there's no way you could ever do that. You think that is the worst possible solution, and that it will only cause problems.

I'm here to tell you that life is too short to let someone or something bother you every day. If someone else is controlling your happiness, that has to be stopped immediately.

So how do you do talk to someone about a problem you're having with him or her? First, you need to logically decide in your head if you've exhausted every other option to make the issue go away. If you have, then it's time to have the talk.

Here is a key point to remember about the talk.

First, it has to be brought up in a business setting and not as a personal attack. Remember, you're an employee of the business, just like the other person is. When the business succeeds, you succeed. When the business runs smoothly, not only is your day better, but also the bottom line of the business becomes a focus rather than putting out fires everywhere.

I told you about my grandpa in an earlier chapter. Again, he was one of the smartest men I ever knew. I wish I had realized just how smart he was when he was alive.

When I was in high school, I was having a disagreement with my girlfriend at the time. On this particular Sunday, when I was visiting with him, we were having nothing but arguments and problems. Ah, teenage love.

He asked me how things were going with her, and I told him not so great. He told me that, if I wanted to stay in that relationship, I needed to do everything I could to work through our problems. He told me when I talked to her next that I needed to keep an open mind, open ears, and use soft words.

Why soft words? I remember him smiling and telling me, "You use soft words because someday you just might have to eat them."

The same holds true in your business. If you're having a tough conversation, you can't approach it with the attitude of, "I'm right. You're wrong. That settles it." No; in order for things to work out, there will need to be an open, honest, and nonemotional discussion.

Let's say you're having a problem with the hygienist. We'll call her Rita. Here's an idea of how to start the conversation.

"Hey, Rita, I know you and I haven't gotten along very well recently. I know we've had some issues and I'm worried that it's going to be something that our patients notice very soon, if they haven't already. I want our business to be the best it can be and for our patients to focus on their oral health while they're in here. Can we find a time to talk?"

You have not only opened the door of communication, but you've also framed it as "what's best for business." It's suddenly not a personal issue, but one that affects your business and your customers.

I have been in a dental practice before when the team wasn't getting along. I've actually been in the chair not long after the dentist and assistant had just had it out. I could feel the tension in the room, and I could hear the instruments being slapped back and forth between the two "dental professionals." It was honestly one of the most uncomfortable moments I've ever experienced. All I could think about during that appointment was, "They're mad at each other, and they're working on my mouth!"

Don't let your patients experience this in your practice. If you walked into a restaurant and could tell almost immediately that the waiter and the chef were having an issue, would you really feel comfortable eating there? If it were me, I'd be wondering what exactly was going into my food. I certainly wouldn't enjoy my experience there, and I'd be very hesitant about going back any time soon.

So, what are some simple tips for getting along better in the practice? Here are three of my favorites.

- **Ask and don't assume.** Have you ever thought someone said something he or she didn't? I would far rather have someone tell me something to my face that I might not like than to say something about me behind my back. If you need to confront someone about something you've heard, use the method above and keep it as a business chat.

- **Avoid controversial topics.** Some of the biggest arguments I have ever seen have resulted from a discussion on politics or religion. Why take a chance on starting something that could turn into an argument? Save your thoughts for outside the business (and please don't talk to your patients about these topics either).

- **Do more listening than talking.** Often, we never really take the time to hear what the other person is saying. We automatically proclaim them guilty for an action. There may be a perfectly good reason why someone leaves early or comes in late. Listen to what the other person has to say before dismissing them as wrong and proclaiming yourself right.

No, we *can't* all just get along. We can, however, all get along *better*. By focusing what could be a hard discussion around what's best for business, you'll find that your days can get easier and happier. Why put that off? Start improving your level of enjoyment at your business today.

Chapter 7

THE DEMON OF "JUST A JOB"

"You need to floss better."

The final demon that needs to be slayed by every dental assistant, no matter how long you've been in your career, is looking at what you do as "just a job."

One thing I often hear from dental assistants about why they love what they do is that every day is different.

Unlike your friends in the hygiene department, you get to do a myriad of things every day to help make an impact on the lives of your patients. You may be assisting with oral surgery in the morning and taking impressions in the afternoon. In between, you may be working on the next order with your local rep or even helping out at the front desk (if you're cross-trained). A dental assistant's work is never done, and your Monday is always different from your Tuesday and your Wednesday.

Yet, despite the ever-changing landscape of your day, many dental assistants still find themselves in a rut. They start listening to the talk that they are "just an assistant." They start believing that they have no power in the practice. They start defeating themselves and sucking away the true power that they have in the business.

That is, of course, what you want to avoid. You can't let the little demon on your shoulder tell you that what you do ultimately doesn't matter. It does.

Dental assistants too often listen to those little voices of doubt, and suddenly dental assisting doesn't seem that great. The greener grass of a career in hygiene starts beckoning to hop the fence and come on over to the other side of the world. Suddenly, being a dental assistant isn't good enough. Suddenly, a dental assisting career is just a stepping stone on the career path toward becoming a hygienist or dentist.

Please understand, I always encourage assistants to pursue their dreams. While I would love for every assistant to stay an assistant for his or her entire career, I also know that that is simply not reality.

If you're pursuing another career after assisting because that's your lifelong dream, that's one thing. But if you want to become a hygienist or dentist simply because the pay is better or you think people will look at you in a different light, that's another topic altogether.

The truth is that you're never "just an assistant" and you never have "just a job." Sit back for a moment and think about all of the patients you have affected during your career. If you really reflect on it and remember all of those faces and smiles, I think you'll be surprised at how long that list might be.

Some assistants tell me that they just don't love what they do. Maybe they've fallen out of love with being a dental assistant. It happens from time to time. I know it does. It's the same reason that so many marriages have problems. Someone gets bored, and suddenly other options look much more appealing.

For assistants, during my presentation I love to ask about what you really love to do during the day. I am always surprised how many assistants tell me that they love the blood and gore that can go along with oral surgery. Hey, that wouldn't be my first choice, but it is for many of you out there.

There's nothing wrong with that, and I think that's great. But my question to you is this: Does your dentist know that that is what you love to do? Have you ever told your dentist how much you love working on a certain procedure or with certain patients? I have seen your eyes literally light up when you talk about helping in an oral surgery procedure. Has your doctor seen that same excitement?

I think it's time that you share your work-related

passions with your dentist. Tell him or her what motivates you and what you love to see pop up on the schedule. This not only starts a conversation about what is important to you in the business, but also reinforces that this isn't "just a job" for you. You've thought about what's important to you, and you know what you love to do. Believe me, that's something that's not common in a lot of industries.

So why all of this work and effort just to reinforce your value? Well, it's simple really. It is a way to show you are proud to be a part of the business in which you're employed and also helps you start to do more of the things that you love to do.

Consider this: from Monday to Thursday (or Friday, depending on when your business shuts down for the week), where do you spend the majority of your waking hours? It's not with your nuclear family. It's with your "work family." Knowing this, why would you just "make it through the day?" I know many people who are employed (both in and out of the dental industry) and simply trying to make it to the weekend. Once Monday starts, they are already counting the seconds until they're done for the day or for the week. That's no way to live.

Do you find yourself in this position? If so, you need to change what's making you feel this way. Often, it's not because you don't love being a dental assistant. It's because you're not getting along with someone in the practice (and that someone could certainly be the dentist). Or it's because you're not being appreciated for the important role you play in the business.

There is a myriad of reasons why you may not currently be enjoying your role in the practice. Only one person can change that dynamic, however, and that's you. You're the one who will need to analyze what you love to do on a daily basis and take steps toward doing more of that. You're the one who may need to have some hard conversations with your coworkers about things that are affecting the business.

Yes, these are not easy conversations. And yes, they are absolutely necessary, sooner rather than later.

Remember this, you are not alone in any of these conversations. There are countless assistants in your town or state or region or throughout the nation who have been there and done that. I promise, whatever demon you are fighting today has already been battled and beaten by some of your colleagues.

The trick is to find those colleagues. Go to your local, state or national dental assisting associations. Reach out to fellow assistants in your town through a mutual introduction by your local sales rep. Join dental assisting groups on Facebook or other social media platforms. Check out IgniteDA.net, a community I started specifically for dental assistants to help them with their daily struggles.

There are resources out there. You just have to do some research and take that big step: introducing yourself. You can do that. It's not as big a step as you might think.

Do you need some confidence to help yourself start changing your career? Here are five things that you can do that won't cost you a penny.

1. **Stop with the putdowns.** That means no negative self-talk and no words like "I'm just a dental assistant."

2. **Lose the "poor me" attitude.** Not everyone is going to respect you or like you. Does that mean you should just resign yourself to being whom they think you are? Absolutely not. Fight against those beliefs. Prove them wrong. Being a victim gets you nowhere.

3. **Grow up.** When I say that, I mean that you should do everything you can to grow in your career. Take those extra classes. Read those extra articles. Make those extra connections. Go above and beyond your job description. How you deal with things and carve your own career path is how you grow.

4. **Take action.** Learn from your mistakes. If you mess up, get better at that procedure. Don't beat yourself up for doing something wrong. Rather, take negative moments and

find a way to turn them into positives down the road. Use mistakes as moments in the rearview mirror at which you look back and think how far you've come in your career.

5. **Believe in yourself.** Remember, if you don't believe in you, who will? You have to stand up straight and project the image of the leader of the practice. You can do that, because you *are* that.

You are an amazing person with a tremendous career ahead of you. Don't let anyone, including yourself, snuff out that flame. You will be amazed at what you can do when you stop listening to the voices who tell you that you can't do it.

Talk to your doctor. Talk to your fellow assistants. Draw strength from them. Step out of your comfort zone. These are the things you must do to grow in your career and become the leader you are destined to be.

Chapter 8

WHAT DOES THE FUTURE HOLD FOR ASSISTANTS?

©Glasbergen
glasbergen.com

"Yes, my teeth react to hot and cold. When it's hot,
they want ice cream. When it's cold, they want cocoa."

Throughout the earlier chapters, we've talked extensively about how you can make your present situation better in the business where you work. But what does the future hold for your profession?

How dentistry changes in the future will impact both your career and your place of employment. Staying ahead of the curve is one of the most important things that any dental assistant can do. Talk to your local rep and pick his or her brain about the latest products and advancements. Read the journals that come into your practice. Attend local or online continuing education courses to stay on the cutting edge. Brainstorm with other dental assistants (either locally or around the nation) on what is working in their practices and trends they see happening.

One of the biggest things that will change your career immediately and continue to change it as years move on is technology. If you've been in the industry for a few years, you've seen major advances that technology has brought to dentistry. Everything from digital X-rays to oral cancer screening to CBCT scans has evolved dramatically, just in the last few years.

Those advances, however, are just the tip of the iceberg. Intraoral scanning and digital impressions will become a bigger and bigger part of a dental practice's everyday routine. I believe 3D printing will become very commonplace in the dental practice as well. I recently attended the International Dental Show meeting in Cologne, Germany, and saw not only a huge rise in the number of 3D printers available from reputable companies you already know, but also materials starting to be developed specifically for 3D crown and bridge printing and more.

That's an exciting development for our industry and for dental assistants as well. State laws will need to keep up with the changes in technology and discuss what role assistants will have in these new areas. What will assistants do with 3D printing? How much can you scan intraorally to help push this technology ahead? There are so many questions yet to be answered, because the technology is moving so quickly.

That's why it is imperative that you stay on top of trends that are out there. You have to know what is coming down the road so you can prepare your career to meet it head on. It's like my favorite quote from the great movie *Ferris Bueller's Day Off*: "Life moves pretty fast. If you don't stop and look around once in a while, you could miss it."[6]

If you don't know what's coming, you absolutely could miss it. I've always heard the metaphorical tale about the frog and the boiling pot of water: If you drop a frog into a boiling pot of water, he'll jump right out because he knows that's not good for him. However, if you have a frog in a pot of water and slowly turn it up, he'll boil to death because he doesn't sense the change that is going on around him.

Obviously, I am not encouraging you to boil a frog any time soon. However, I think you get my point with the analogy. If you're not aware of your surroundings, you could find yourself in trouble sooner than you think.

I think dental assistants also need to be aware of the rise of group practices and how that will change our industry. I have talked throughout much of this book about how dental practices need to be operated as businesses. That's exactly what has driven group practices to the forefront in many states. Working as a

---

[6] *Ferris Bueller's Day Off*. Directed by John Hughes. 1986.

business, group practices are able to be efficient when it comes to everything from purchasing supplies to scheduling patients.

Dental assistants should understand that working for a group practice is different than working in a traditional practice. The dentist with whom you may work at the group practice probably isn't the owner of the practice. He or she is an employee, just like you. It may make some of those conversations we've discussed between you and the dentist take on a different spin, since he or she may not be the final decision maker.

I am neither advocating for nor opposing group practices when I talk about them. Each individual must decide whether that is the right environment for him or her. I do, however, believe it would be best to talk to an assistant who is already working in a group practice to get a feel for potential differences in that working environment. It's always smart to do as much research as you can before entering into a new venture. Asking an assistant who already works in a group practice what he or she likes and dislikes about it is a great way to do some personal research to help you make a decision.

Another trend we're seeing in the industry is the rise of the female dentist. It's estimated that by 2020, there will be more female dentists working in the industry than males. That's a huge paradigm shift from the past. It will also make the dental practice a female-dominated place. If you're a male dental assistant reading this book, you already know you're in the vast minority in your industry. Overall, it's estimated that females hold 95 percent of the jobs when it comes to assisting and hygiene. Now, with females overtaking their male counterparts for the majority of dentist jobs by the end of the decade, you can see why dentistry is quickly becoming even more of a woman's world.

I don't consider this trend a bad thing at all. For centuries, women have been seen as more caring and nurturing. In a place like a dental practice, where patients are often resistant to go, it's a psychological benefit to know that someone is waiting who will treat you with care. Now, obviously, that's a broad statement. Not all female dentists are more caring than their male counterparts. But if a patient feels more comfortable walking into your business (for whatever reason), that's a good thing for your bottom line. It will change the way patients view your business and could also change your interpersonal dynamics in the practice.

Plenty of shifts are happening in today's dental landscape. Some of them will impact your career dramatically. Whatever you do and whatever your passion might be, please don't fall into the trap of thinking, "I'll learn about that later," or "That will never happen in my practice." Things can change in the blink of an eye when it comes to your employment. Your doctor may sell the practice or suddenly no longer be able to work. You should always be prepared for the possibility of change. Sitting on your hands and putting things off will not prepare you for that.

What's the best advice I can give you about what the future will hold for you and dentistry? Become an expert in the latest technology. Ask questions. Push your boundaries. Be resourceful. These are the things that will drive your success as we move into the next decade.

A dental assistant once told me after a lecture that she and her doctor planned to retire together. They learned the same things at the same pace. They made plans for their continuing education (CE) together and decided what things would be best for their business. It seemed perfect—until the doctor was killed one night in an auto accident. She suddenly realized that all the plans he had been making were going to benefit him much more than her.

When the new dentist took over the practice, she realized just how slowly she had taken things because she had been comfortable with the former dentist taking the lead on when and where CE would happen and what techniques they would learn. The appearance of a new dentist brought a new atmosphere to the practice. She quickly learned that she was behind the times.

Don't get too comfortable at what you're doing. It's easy to sit back and just take things as they come rather than chasing them down. The easiest road, however, is not always the best road.

It's much like a goldfish swimming in its bowl. Think about all of the pet goldfish you've known in your life. Did you know that if you took the goldfish out of the bowl and let them swim around a lake, they would grow to a bigger size? The thing that keeps pet goldfish from growing is the size of the bowl that they live in.

What's your bowl? What's keeping you from growing to the size that you should be in your career? Figure out what your bowl is and break out of it before it is too late. Your future and your career depend on it.

Chapter 9

FIVE THINGS THAT WILL BOOST YOUR CAREER

©Glasbergen
glasbergen.com

"Yes, I floss regularly — right before every appointment."

So, what are the important things that you need to do to maintain and improve your career? Here are my five main thoughts.

Establish Communication

You need to ensure that your working relationships with your dentist and teammates within the business are as strong as possible. To make this happen, you have to do everything you can to make your feelings heard and eliminate any gossip or tension within the business.

If you know of a problem developing between you and the doctor or you and another team member, solve the issue sooner rather than later. You can't let things bubble around the surface until they explode. Think about a splinter. If you get one in your finger, you want to get it out as soon as possible. If you let the splinter just stay in your finger, infection and pain will set in. Getting it out as soon as possible is important to your health.

This holds true for you emotionally, as well. If you're holding something inside, it's only going to fester and get worse. Take the steps necessary to have conversations about things that aren't going well. Always frame these conversations in the context of what is best for business rather than letting things get emotional or personal.

Communication also includes talking to your doctor about what motivates you to become better at what you do. Your doctor may *think* he or she knows what you love to do and why you're an assistant, but is that truly the case, or is it a guessing game?

Open up a conversation about it. Ask questions. See how you can get better. See how you can do more of what you love to do on a daily basis. The more you talk about things, the more you'll learn, and the more the doctor will understand about you. It's not a tough conversation to have, but it's one that you have to make sure isn't just one-sided. Talk about your passions, but also ask questions and listen to what is being said in response. Listening is just as important as explaining your side of things.

When a conversation about passions and interests begins, it can spark into further and deeper conversations about future hopes, dreams, and goals. Take advantage of this opportunity to connect on a deeper level and explain why you love to do what you do every day.

Do Some Research

Go to DANB.org and look up the great resources that the Dental Assisting National Board provides for you. Learn your state laws and know what you legally can or can't do in your state. Look up what it will take for you to earn assisting credentials in your state. This is a must-visit site for any dental assistant.

Also, do some research on what learning programs are available to you, either online or in your geographic area. Ask your sales rep what he or she knows. Ask your dental assisting colleagues what has worked for them. Make time in your schedule to not only do the research but then follow up and attend the online and/or in-person courses.

Go the Extra Step

This follows along with the last point, but don't be content with doing the same things the same way you've always done them. Learn what's new. Explore new techniques and products. Ask a question if you don't think you fully understand what was just said.

Western writer Louis L'Amour is credited with once having said, "Nobody got anywhere in the world by simply being content." I love that quote.

I get restless if I do the same thing the same way for too long. I'm always wanting to see what's new and what's going to keep me on top of my game. If I never did any research and just kept presenting the same lecture to dental assistants, people would get bored, and my material would become outdated quickly. It's key for me always to be looking for the latest statistics and figures that I can share with my audience in the dental industry. The same should be true for you with your patients.

Don't Be Afraid

Many assistants have told me they won't start conversations with their dentists because they're worried they'll be rejected or humiliated. Assistants won't talk to the hygienist who are giving them problems because it might blow up into something bigger than it already is. Assistants won't suggest something new in a team meeting because other team members might laugh at them.

You can't live in a *what if* world. You can't constantly be saying, "Yes, but what if…" or you will paralyze yourself with possibilities. Don't let the *what if* keep you from moving ahead in your career or with a conversation that needs to be had. A *what if* moment hasn't happened yet, and may not happen at all. If a potential scenario you're playing out in your head is keeping you from doing something you need to do, ignore those inner doubts.

A *what if* can be a death knell for your creativity or passion. Don't let it make you a victim. Take a chance and step out of your comfort zone. It's the only way to move forward.

In a 2005 commencement speech to graduates of Stanford University, Apple cofounder Steve Jobs said, "Your time is limited, so don't waste it living someone else's life. Don't be trapped by dogma—which is living with the results of other people's thinking. Don't let the noise of others' opinions drown out your own inner voice. And most important, have the courage to follow your heart and intuition."[7]

---

[7] Stanford University. "Text of Steve Jobs' Commencement Address (2005)." Stanford News. September 15, 2016.

Truer words have never been spoken.

Be the Best Darn *You* You Can Be

One time on *Saturday Night Live,* Steve Martin broke into song about how he was going to be the best darned *me* that he could be. It was a hilarious song and skit that I still remember quite well.

Here are part of his lyrics that night.

> "And nothing's gonna stop me!
> 'Cause I'm somebody!
> That's right! I'm me!
> I'm not you, or you, or you, or you!
> I'm me!
> I'm gonna climb to the top of the tree!
> I'm gonna ford that stream!
> Gonna make all the world mine!
> That's right!
> And nobody's gonna stop me!"[8]

I remember the skit vividly because Martin suddenly

---

[8] Chevy Chase, Steve Martin & Martin Short's Monologue. Accessed May 15, 2017. http://snltranscripts.jt.org/86/86fmono.phtml.

realized how important that he was and that he could actually accomplish whatever he set out to do.

That's exactly what I wish for all dental assistants. It's not a matter of trying to imitate someone else or do things exactly the way you heard in a lecture one time. You're not a robot. You're a human being who has a brilliant mind.

Take the best of what you've heard in lectures and/ or read in this book and mold them around your personality and work skills. You already have amazing talents. Now take those talents to the proverbial "next level" through your acquisition of skills and knowledge.

Becoming the best darned you that you can be will take some time and energy and work on your part, but I don't believe we were put on this planet just to be OK at what we did, or just OK with how we feel about our day-to-day work or career. OK isn't good enough in my book. Settling for OK just doesn't work. OK has the stench of stagnation attached to it.

Don't settle for being OK at what you do or having an OK career. Have the best day and career that you can possibly have. Break out of your shell of comfort and stretch your boundaries. Do that, and you're on your way to becoming the best darned you that you can be.

Chapter 10

FINAL THOUGHTS AND MOTIVATION

"I can give you a whitening treatment,
but I make no guarantees."

Someone asked me one time why I enjoyed working with dental assistants so much. The simple truth of the matter is that I feel dental assistants make the dental practice run, yet get too little recognition for everything they do on a daily basis.

When I first came into the dental industry, I knew nothing about dentistry. Coming from sports public relations into this field, I was trying to do everything I could to learn as much as I could about what goes on in a dental practice and in the dental industry, so I could communicate with all members of the dental team in a coherent way.

I remember one time I was talking to a dentist for an article I was writing for *Dental Economics*. I was fairly new in the industry at the time. About halfway through the conversation, the person I was interviewing paused and asked me, "Do you even know what I am talking about? Are you a dentist?" I told him I was not and started to explain my background. In a huff, he interrupted me and said, "If you're not a dentist, why am I wasting my time talking to you?" With that, he hung up on me. I was stunned. I was mad. Then my anger turned to wondering if I was ever going to be able to do my job correctly and be respected for what I did.

I know you've had days like this as well. You've had days when you dropped an instrument tray or had the dentist glare at you during a procedure. You feel about two inches tall, and it's the worst feeling in the world. I get that.

But you know what? It's not about the mistake or the glare or the feelings that come right after it. It's what you do next.

A buddy of mine and I were playing golf one time, and I hit my ball into the sand trap. I had been playing a really solid round of golf, but this one shot threatened to blow up my entire game. I was mumbling to myself as I walked toward the trap. My buddy yelled at me from across the course and said, "You know, in golf, it's not about the last shot. It's about the next shot."

He was right. There was nothing I could do about the shot I had hit into the bunker. What was I going to do about getting the ball *out* of the bunker? That's the bigger question. I could have let one mistake ruin my entire game. But when I focused on the next shot, I was able to get back on track.

Roman Emperor Marcus Aurelius said, "You have power over your mind—not outside events. Realize this, and you will find strength."[9] Whatever has happened in your past is in the past. Whatever problems you have had in your career are in the past. Whatever demons of dental assisting have jumped at you and tried to pull you off your career path are behind you. Today starts a new chapter. It's not about the last shot. It's about the next shot.

One of the reasons I love talking to dental assistants is because of who you are and all of the potential that lies inside each of you. You have a Cinderella quality about you. You've done all of the cleaning and errands and things that no one else in the practice might want to do. You've had people say you will only be an assistant. You've had folks look down their noses at you. Emotionally, they've tried to lock you in the tallest tower. That's in the past, I believe. I see each of you, not as the tired and ash-ridden Cinderella, but rather as the princess finally getting into a beautiful gown and heading to the ball.

Why? Because I have seen the amazing things you do for your patients. I have seen the patience that you all have

---

9   Aurelius, Marcus, and George Long. *The Meditations of Marcus Aurelius*. London: Watkins, 2006.

with everyone, from the dentist to the denture patient. I have seen the kindness in your eyes and witnessed the love you express through a smile, or a hug, or a handshake.

Why do I talk to dental assistants around the country? Why did I write this book? Why will I keep being your biggest cheerleader? Because I believe in you. I believe in the power you have to impact your patients, and to change the dynamics of your business and the entire industry.

I believe in you. I appreciate you. I admire you. Now you just have to believe in yourself and the power that you hold.

You can do it. Make the change in your mindset today. I can't wait to hear your stories of success and inspiration.

Appendix A
ACKNOWLEDGEMENTS

....

I wouldn't be who I am without my family's support and love. I mentioned my grandpa several times in this book. My grandparents and parents taught me not only to respect other people, but also to really listen to what they have to say. I'm eternally grateful for the lessons they taught me, even when I was too stubborn to listen. I love you all.

Thank you to my wife and best friend, Dayna, who has always encouraged me to pursue my dreams and been there to share in my joys and disappointments. I love you more.

Thank you to my daughter, Julia. You've always loved your dad, no matter what. For that, I will always be grateful. Being your dad has been the greatest blessing of my life. Love you tons.

Thank you to Lyle Hoyt and Mark Hartley for taking a chance on a sports PR guy to be your next editor of *Proofs* magazine. I wouldn't be in dentistry without you, and that decision changed my life forever.

There are many friends and colleagues in the industry I could thank. It's impossible to name you all. I am indebted, however, to Linda Miles, Tija Hunter, and Mary Govoni. Each of them has shown me the power that assistants can have in so many areas of the industry.

Lastly, thank you to the countless assistants out there I have met through the years. You inspire me every day. I hope I can return the favor to you.

Appendix B
RESOURCES

IgniteDA (http://www.IgniteDA.net)

Dental Assisting National Board (http://www.danb.org)

Bureau of Labor Statistics (http://www.bls.gov)

NINJA Dentistry (http://www.ninjadentistry.com)

Appendix C

ABOUT THE AUTHOR

A n advocate of today's dental assistant, Kevin Henry speaks to dental audiences across the nation on topics that empower dental assistants, helping them to recognize the leadership role they hold in the practice. He is the co-founder of IgniteDA.net, a community designed to enlighten, empower, and engage dental assistants to help them reach their full potential and flourish in their careers.

With seventeen years in the dental publishing industry, Kevin is the former founding voice and editor behind *Dental Assisting Digest* and *Modern Dental Assistant.* He is the former group editorial director for *Dental Products Report* and managing editor for *Dental Economics.* He was recently named as one of the top five influential voices in the industry on Twitter (@kgh23).

In Kevin's former life, he was a public relations director for NAIA, a national small college sports organization. He is currently a beat writer for the Colorado Rockies and a former beat writer for the Denver Nuggets. Living in Colorado, Kevin loves to be outdoors with his wife and friends, whether it be hiking, skiing, or white-water rafting. Kevin can be contacted for bulk sales of this book or for speaking engagements at 918-613-1188 or by e-mail at kevin@kevinspeaksdental.com.

Made in the USA
Lexington, KY
29 May 2018